POETRY WRITING ACTIVITIES for MIDDLE SCHOOL

"As blue as a rainy day without a friend"

CLARK STEVENS

Illustrations by Evelyn Winter

 J. Weston Walch, Publisher

Portland, Maine

1   2   3   4   5   6   7   8   9   10

ISBN 0-8251-2499-9

Copyright © 1994
J. Weston Walch, Publisher
P. O. Box 658 • Portland, Maine 04104-0658

Printed in the United States of America

Contents

Note to the Student

Sometimes when you write a poem, it's like solving a puzzle or playing a game.

Sometimes writing a poem is like making a joke.

At still other times, writing a poem gives you a way to say something that just doesn't want to be said any other way—not in a talk with a friend, not in a letter, not even in a painting or a song or a dance. Sometimes you just have to write a poem.

This book will introduce you to some of the many ways a poem can be written. You'll see some funny poem forms and some serious ones, some very short ones and some longer ones. Some will be written in set patterns, others will be free-form. After you read each kind of poem, you'll follow the step-by-step guidance and write a poem like that of your own.

Then the next time you have something to say that just doesn't want to be said in any way but a poem, you'll know just the kind of poem to write.

Whether you feel full of "joy" that "can't sit still" (Activity 20) or "as blue as a rainy day without a friend" (Activity 16), write a poem!

—**The Editors**

I. GETTING STARTED

Numbers Poem

Many short and easy poems can be made from simple *lists*. Try your hand at the Numbers Poem activity below.

Step One

- Pick a number between one and twelve—for example, six.

- Write your number in the space provided at the top of the following page as a title for your poem.

- Now try to brainstorm a list of at least twelve lines of your poem that contain your number.

  Each line can begin with your number:

  ```
  Six friends talking at a party
  Six winter coats on the coatrack
  ```

  Or the line can contain your number somewhere within the line:

  ```
  I spotted six black bears
  Trapped on a planet with six suns
  ```

  Your list can be made up of twelve nonrelated lines:

  ```
  Six slimy snakes/Six bright stars/
  Six dropping flowers/etc.
  ```

  Or you can try to make all the lines relate to one subject:

  ```
  Six soldiers trudging/Over six days/
  With only six cans of food for all/etc.
  ```

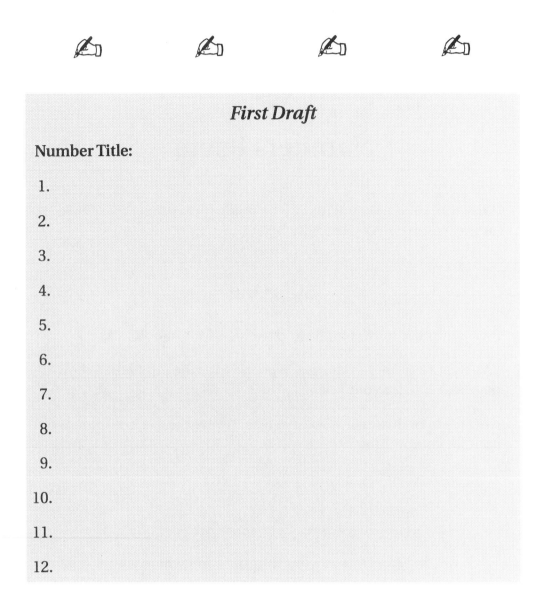

Number Title:

1.

2.

3.

4.

5.

6.

7.

8.

9.

10.

11.

12.

Step Two

Now, you can begin to work on the final draft of your Numbers Poem.

● First, quietly read each of your lines to yourself.

● Which lines seem most interesting or imaginative? Which lines sound best?

● Put a star (*) next to the lines that you like most and might like to include in your final poem.

● In the final version of your poem, you don't have to use all twelve lines from your first draft—just the lines that seem right to you.

● When you write your final choices below, also feel free to change your original order:

Which lines sound good or make sense together?

Which line would make a good first line?

Which would make a good last line?

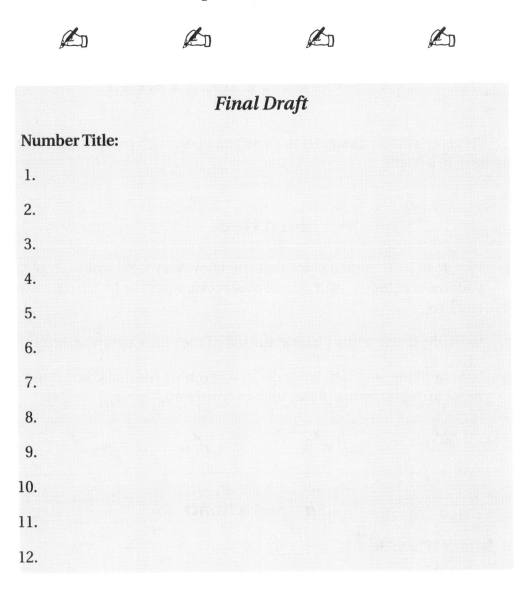

Final Draft

Number Title:

1.

2.

3.

4.

5.

6.

7.

8.

9.

10.

11.

12.

Step Three

When your Numbers Poem is complete, read it again quietly to yourself. Then, if you are willing, share it with a classmate or with your whole class.

Listen to other students' Numbers Poems. How are they like yours? How are they different?

Seven-Word Place Poem

This is an activity designed to show you how much power single words can have in a poem.

Step One

- Picture in your mind a place that you know very well—for example, your room at home, your school classroom, a park or beach near where you live.

- Write the name of the place at the top of the space below as a title.

- Now, working very fast, write the first seven words that come into your mind to describe that place, such as "cluttered," "noisy," "empty."

First Seven Words

Name of Place Here:

1.

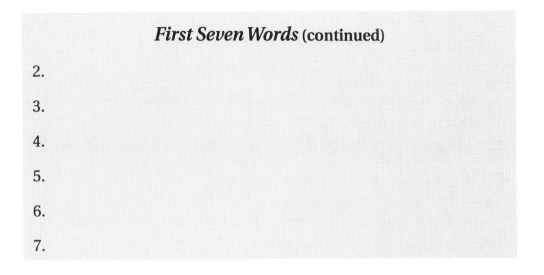

First Seven Words (continued)

2.

3.

4.

5.

6.

7.

Step Two

- Now reread your list of single words quietly to yourself.

- Which words best capture the place you have chosen? Which words seem weakest? Circle the best words.

Step Three

- Now, in the space below, work fast to come up with seven entirely new words to describe the place you have chosen to write about. Don't repeat any of the words in your first list.

Next Seven Words

Name of Place Here:

1.

2.

(continued)

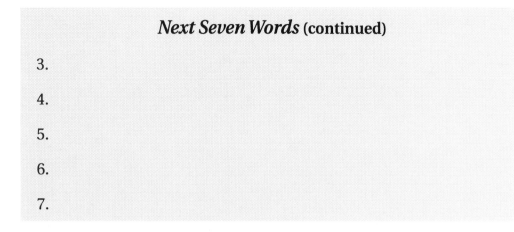

Next Seven Words (continued)

3.

4.

5.

6.

7.

Step Four

- Read this second list quietly aloud. Circle those words that work best.

- You can now begin to work on your final Seven-Word Place Poem.

- Look at the circled words on both of your lists. Put a star by the seven best words to include in your final poem.

- If you think you still need more good words to complete the seven, let new words come into your mind to help you complete the poem.

- Finally, choose the best order for your final words. Which word should go first? Which word should go last? Which words belong together in the middle?

- Remember, there are no right or wrong answers. The choices are entirely up to you. It's your poem.

- When you are ready, write your finished poem in the space below.

Final Poem

Name of Place Here:

1.

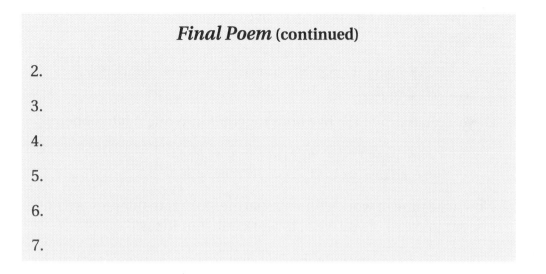

Final Poem (continued)

2.

3.

4.

5.

6.

7.

Step Five

● Read your finished poem quietly to yourself. Then, without giving the title, read it to a friend or to your whole class. Can your listener(s) guess the place that you are describing in your poem?

③

Writing with Your Senses

Many effective poems make use of the five senses: seeing, hearing, touching, tasting, and smelling. Try to make use of your senses in the activity below.

This exercise is a PAIR activity. Before moving on to the instructions below, the class should break into groups of two.

Step One

● In this activity, the job of each pair of writers is to write a five-line non-rhyming poem in which each line features a different sense.

● The five lines can be made up of five completely unrelated sense images:

```
I like the taste of hot cocoa on a cold day.
Did you see the blue jay in the tree?
```

● Or you can try to fit the five lines together into one related poem:

```
I can smell the springtime roses—
They shine bright red in the sun.
```

● Now, take time to work with your partner to create lines for your poem. Use scrap paper, if you wish, to work out your ideas.

● When you are ready, write the first draft of your Senses Poem in the space provided in both partners' activity texts.

First Draft

1.

2.

3.

4.

5.

Step Two

● Next, the partners of each pair should read their poem draft quietly to themselves.

● Each partner should underline the words, images, or lines that seem strongest.

● Each partner should also look at the words, images, or lines that don't seem as strong. Can you explain why they are weaker?

● One reason could be that these expressions are what are called **clichés** (klee-SHAYS)—expressions that are so overused that they have lost their power. An example is:

    `The sunrise was very beautiful to see.`

● Each partner should circle any clichés in the first draft. Compare your findings with each other.

● Now work together to see if you can find ways to make these expressions more original. A new example might be:

    `The sunrise was as bright as a child's eyes.`

● As a team, make any final changes you would like in your Senses Poem. Then copy it in the space provided in both partners' workbooks.

● If you wish, give your final poem a title.

Final Draft

1.

2.

3.

4.

5.

Step Three

● When your Senses Poem is complete, decide which partner is to read it to another team or to your whole class.

Listen to other teams' poems. Have others done a good job of including the five senses in their poems? Have they done a good job of eliminating clichés?

4

Diamond Poem

Sometimes being forced to write a poem within a set pattern actually frees a poet's creativity. Give the Diamond Poem a try, and see for yourself.

Step One

- This first Diamond Poem is intended as a warm-up exercise.

- Notice how the grid is laid out in the space below: thinnest at the top and bottom and widest at the middle.

- First, write the starter word "Sun" on the single blank line for number 1.

- Now, working quickly from top to bottom, fill in a single word in each remaining blank line of the grid to create a Diamond Poem.

- Don't try to have your poem make sense. Let your imagination lead the poem wherever it wants to go:

```
        Sun
      Such fun
  Brighter than night
    Hot as a gun
```

- Your lines can include rhyme, like the example above, but they don't have to:

```
        Sun
     Is singing
  Is shining light
   Will burn you
        too
```

Warm-up Draft

1. _____

2. _____   _____

3. _____   _____   _____

4. _____   _____   _____   _____

5. _____   _____   _____   _____   _____

6. _____   _____   _____   _____

7. _____   _____   _____

8. _____   _____

9. _____

Step Two

- Take a moment to read your warm-up draft to yourself.

- Circle the lines or word combinations that you like best.

- Why do you like them? Do they create an interesting image or idea? Do they sound good together?

- Next, underline the words or lines you would like to change. Decide on changes you could make to improve them.

● When you are ready, write your final warm-up poem in the space below.

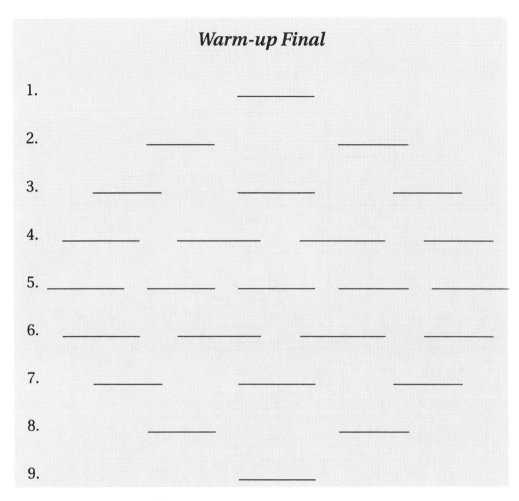

Warm-up Final

1. _____

2. _____   _____

3. _____   _____   _____

4. _____   _____   _____   _____

5. _____   _____   _____   _____   _____

6. _____   _____   _____   _____

7. _____   _____   _____

8. _____   _____

9. _____

Step Three

● Now it's time for you to create a Diamond Poem on a subject of your own choice.

● First, choose your own starter word. Write it on the single line for number 1.

● Now work to fill in the rest of the empty lines in the grid.

First Draft

1. _____   _____

2. _____   _____

3. _____   _____   _____

4. _____   _____   _____   _____

5. _____   _____   _____   _____   _____

6. _____   _____   _____   _____

7. _____   _____   _____

8. _____   _____

9. _____

Step Four

● Take a moment to review your draft.

● What changes could you make to improve the poem?

● When you are ready, copy your final version into the grid on the following page.

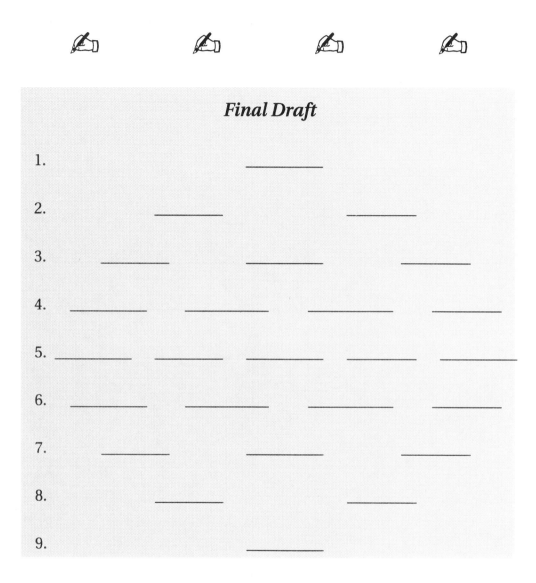

Step Five

● First, read your poem aloud to classmates. Then let them look at how it appears on the page.

Observation Poem

Good poems often spring from careful observation. You can learn a great deal about a person, place, or thing by observing that subject over a period of time.

Step One

● Pick a person, place, or thing to observe—a family member, a place near where you live, or your bicycle, for example.

● At a time when you are feeling relaxed and open, take time to observe your subject.

● Have a sheet of paper and pencil handy so that you can take notes about what you see.

● Your goal is to have at least twenty different observations about your subject.

● Afterwards, in the space below, begin to list all the things that you noticed about your subject.

● Each observation should be phrased in a complete sentence.

● And each observation should contain as many strong details as possible to give a clear and vivid picture to your reader. For example:

```
       OK:  My father has a loud laugh.

   BETTER:  My father's laugh is so loud it even
            wakes up the cat.

       OK:  It was windy in the park today.

   BETTER:  The wind in the park blew so hard every-
            one had to walk backwards.
```

OK: The wheels on my new bicycle are red and silver.

BETTER: With their red rims and silver spokes, my wheels look as if they're on fire when I speed on my new bike.

Observation List

1.

2.

3.

4.

5.

6.

7.

8.

9.

10.

11.

12.

13.

14.

15.

16.

17.

Observation List (continued)

18.

19.

20.

Write additional observations on an extra sheet of paper.

Step Two

● When you have completed your list, take a few moments to look it over.

● Put a check mark by the observations that seem most interesting or sound best.

● Your Observation Poem may include up to twelve lines. Decide which observations you would like to include.

● Next, decide the order in which you will list them in your poem draft. Write your first draft in the space below.

First Draft

1.

2.

3.

4.

(continued)

First Draft (continued)

5.

6.

7.

8.

9.

10.

11.

12.

Step Three

- Take a moment to quietly read aloud the first draft of your Observation Poem.

- Could you make any changes in the phrasing of any observation sentence that would make it more interesting or better-sounding?

- Could your poem be improved by changing the order in which you have placed the sentences?

- When you have finished with your revisions, write your final draft in the space on the next page.

- If you wish, feel free to add an appropriate title.

Final Draft

1.

2.

3.

4.

5.

6.

7.

8.

9.

10.

11.

12.

Step Four

● Read your Observation Poem to a classmate or to your whole class. Do your listeners agree that you have done a good job capturing your subject?

6

Five-Feelings Poem

Feelings play a major role in many poems. Most often it is a poet's feelings that inspire him or her to create a poem.

This exercise is a SMALL-GROUP activity. Before moving on to the instructions below, the class should break into groups of three or four.

Step One

- In the space below, each member of each group should write five feeling sentences about the Fourth of July.

- Each sentence should contain a different feeling about the Fourth of July, such as:

    ```
    The fireworks make me feel patriotic.
    My baby brother is scared by the noises.
    We are all very tired the next day.
    ```

- Try to be honest about your true feelings, and also be as specific as possible:

    NOT: I like sparklers on the Fourth.

    BETTER: I like the way you can draw circles in
             the dark with sparklers.

Five-Feelings List

1.

2.

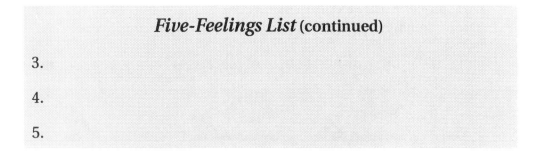

Five-Feelings List (continued)

3.

4.

5.

Step Two

● After each group member has written five feeling sentences, take turns reading them to other members of your group.

● Ask your group members to tell you which of your sentences work best for them and to try to explain why.

Are the feelings honest and clearly presented?

Does the sentence create a vivid and specific picture?

● Then ask your group members to tell you which of your sentences don't work for them and ask them to explain why.

● Listen carefully. Others may have valuable ideas for helping you improve your sentences. But remember, too, the final choices are yours to make.

● After all group members have had a chance to have the group review their sentences, go on to work individually to write your own Fourth of July Five-Feelings Poem.

Step Three

● In deciding how to write your first draft, you may choose either to:

1) Revise the weak sentences in your list above

2) Or write new sentences to replace them.

● When you have finished making all changes in your sentences, choose the order in which you will use them best in your poem.

● Finally, write your finished Fourth of July Five-Feelings Poem draft in the space below.

First Draft

1.

2.

3.

4.

5.

Step Four

● As in Step Two, students should take turns reading their drafts to other members of their group.

● Again, ask other students what they like and dislike about your draft.

● After all group members have had a chance to have the group review their drafts, go on to work individually to write the final draft of your own Fourth of July Five-Feelings Poem.

● Make revisions as described in Step Three and then write your final poem in the space on the following page.

Step Five

● When your Fourth of July Five-Feelings Poem is complete, share it with your entire class. How many different feelings about the Fourth of July did all the poets in your class come up with?

One-Sentence Poem

Many good poems are created out of a very few words. Did you know that you can make a poem out of a single sentence?

Step One

● To start your One-Sentence Poem, first write a starter sentence on the next page that contains exactly *ten* words. Here's an example:

```
My cat is black and has very, very sharp claws.
```

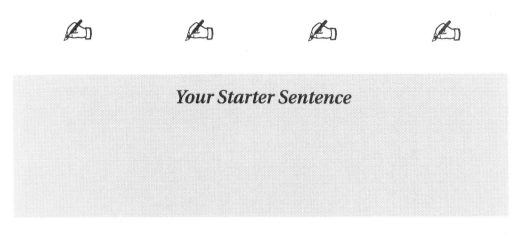

Your Starter Sentence

Step Two

● Now, look at your starter sentence.

● Where do the natural breaks in the sentence fall?

● Mark off the breaks with diagonal slash marks:

```
My cat/ is black/ and has/ very,/ very/ sharp
claws.
```

● Don't worry if you see more than one way to break up your sentence. Just choose one way.

Step Three

● Now, try writing your starter sentence in poem form in the space below, following your slash marks above.

● Try to use no more than three words in any line. For example:

```
My cat
is black
and has
very,
very
sharp claws.
```

At this point, you may also revise your starter sentence in any way you choose to make a better poem.

Get rid of weak verbs, such as "is"

Add stronger adjectives and adverbs

Make your sentence create a vivid picture or tell a story, as in:

```
My black
cat
scratches
fiercely
with
very,
very
sharp claws.
```

Remember, however, your sentence still must stay at exactly ten words.

First Draft

Step Four

● Now, try breaking up your starter sentence in a different way.

You might try using more or fewer words in each line:

```
My
black
cat
scratches.
```

Or you may try varying the number of words, line by line:

```
My
black cat
scratches
fiercely with
very,
very sharp
claws.
```

● Write the second version of your One-Sentence Poem in the space below.

Second Draft

Step Five

● Now, quietly read your first and second drafts to yourself.

● Does the different arrangement of words on the page change the meaning? How?

  Do you like one version better than another?

  Are there specific lines in each version that seem best to you?

  Do any new changes occur to you that you would like to make?

● Finally, combine all the elements that work best to create your final One-Sentence Poem.

Final Draft

Step Six

- Exchange your two drafts and the final version of your One-Sentence Poem with one other classmate. Do you each agree that your final drafts are the best versions?

  If your classmate prefers one of your earlier drafts, ask him or her to explain why.

Questions Poem

You can write a very original poem by brainstorming a list of questions and then editing and ordering them into a final Questions Poem.

This exercise is a WHOLE-CLASS activity that the entire class can work on together.

Step One

● In order to create a class Questions Poem, you each need to compose a list of ten questions on your own.

● Let the questions come randomly in an unconnected list that doesn't need to make sense—for example:

```
Why is the sky blue?

Where's the toothpaste?

Is New York City in New York State?
```

● Work fast. Write your questions in the space that follows.

Questions List

1.

2.

3.

4.

Step Two

- Now, take a look at your questions.

- Mark the questions you like best with a star (*).

    Which do you like because of how they sound?

    Which do you like because they are questions that truly interest you?

    Which do you like just because they're "crazy"?

- Feel free to make changes in the phrasing of any question.

Step Three

- Now, pick your three favorite questions and write them on separate pieces of paper.

- A member of your class should collect all the question slips and place them in a hat or box.

- Next, a student should randomly pick a question from the collection, go to the blackboard, and write the question on the board.

● This same process continues until eight different students have pulled out eight questions and written them on the board.

● In this way the class has generated the first draft of a random Questions Poem.

Step Four

● For the final stage, students go back to working on their own.

● Look at the Questions Poem on the blackboard as if it were the rough draft of your own poem.

What lines would you leave as they are?

What lines would you change? (In this exercise you can't add new lines at this stage.)

What lines would you decide not to use at all? (In *your* final poem you may choose to use any number of the eight lines available.)

● When you have made your choices and all the changes you wish, decide on a final order for your finished lines and write them in the following space.

● If you wish, add an appropriate title at the top of your poem.

Final Draft

1.

2.

3.

4.

5.

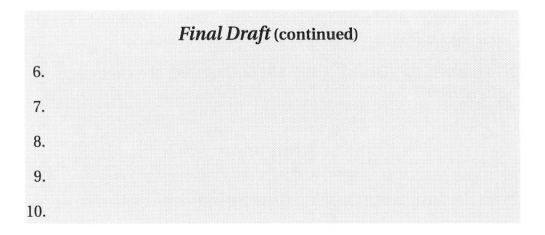

Step Five

● When your final Questions Poem is complete, share it with your class. How did other class members combine the random questions generated by the class to create their own original poems?

Lake Fish   *Evelyn Winter*

II. *Playing Around with Sound*

"S-S" Poem

Poets make use of combining the sounds of words in many ways. One technique is putting words together that have the same first consonant sound, such as <u>big</u> <u>b</u>oat. This technique is called **alliteration**.

Step One

● The "S-S" Poem that follows makes use of the technique of alliteration.

● First, in the space on the next page, write a list of twelve two-word combinations in which each word begins with the letter "S." For example:

```
smart student or slippery slide
```

The first word is an adjective, a word that describes another—such as "smart" or "slippery."

The second word is a noun, the word that is being described—such as "student" or "slide."

The combinations can make sense:

```
strong safe
soft slipper
sly snake
```

Or they can just be random pairs of "S" words:

```
silent soup
silly sofa
salty sunburn
```

● Work as fast as you can and write your pairs in the space below.

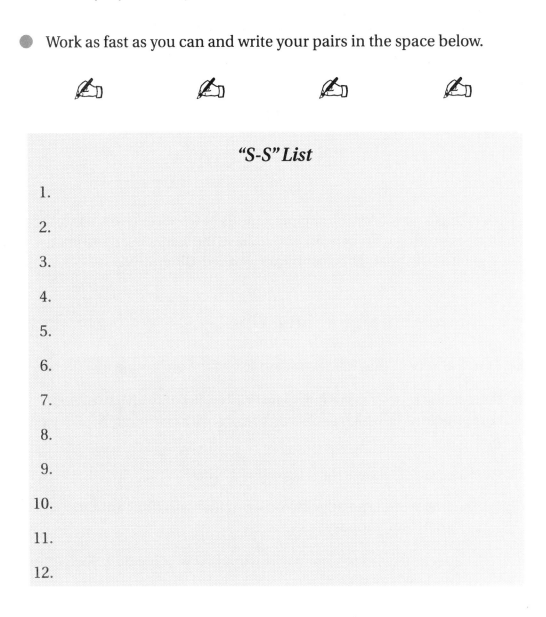

"S-S" List

1.

2.

3.

4.

5.

6.

7.

8.

9.

10.

11.

12.

Step Two

● Now, take a look at your "S-S" combinations.

● Which pairs are the most interesting? Which sound best? Which make the most surprising combinations?

● Choose the combinations you would like to use in your final poem—at least six—and decide on the order you'll write them in the space provided.

● Remember that your final poem does not have to make sense at all.

> ### *Final Draft*

Step Three

● When your final "S-S" Poem is complete, share it with your class. When you listen to the "S-S" Poems written by the rest of your classmates, make a list of the combinations that you think work best. Can you explain why?

⑩

"—oo—/—oo—" Poem

One of the many ways that poets make use of sound in poetry is by putting words together that have the same inner vowel sound—for example, "m<u>oo</u>n" and "h<u>oo</u>t". This technique is called **assonance**.

This exercise is a PAIR activity. Before moving on to the instructions below, the class should break into groups of two.

Step One

● This "—oo—/—oo—" Poem makes use of assonance, which is the effect created by putting together words that have the same inner vowel sounds.

● First, working with your partner, make a list of as many words as you can that share the same inner "oo" vowel sound as the word "m<u>oo</u>n."

  Some of your words may rhyme with moon, such as "s<u>oo</u>n," but there are many other eligible words that won't rhyme, such as "h<u>oo</u>t."

  Also, the words do not have to be spelled with "oo" as long as they share the same sound, as in "flute" or "new."

● The words can be one syllable (n<u>ew</u>), two syllables (l<u>u</u>nar), or three syllables (macar<u>oo</u>n).

● Brainstorm with your partner to create as long a list as you can. Each of you should write your team's entire list on your own book page.

● Don't include the preceding examples in your list.

"oo" List

_____

_____

_____

_____

_____

_____

_____

_____

_____

_____

_____

Step Two

- Now, take a look at your "oo" word list. From this list you and your partner are going to create a poem of total assonance, in which every word will share at least one inner vowel sound that is the same.

- The poem grid on the following page has eight lines. In each line, you have the choice of inserting one, two, or three words from your list above.

● Look at your list. Which words would be most meaningful together? Which words would sound best together? Which would make the most surprising combinations?

● Work together with your partner to choose the combinations you would like to use and write a draft of your eight-line "oo/oo" Poem below.

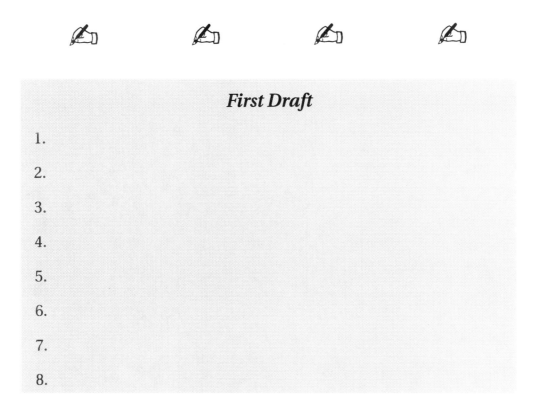

First Draft

1.

2.

3.

4.

5.

6.

7.

8.

Step Three

● Now that you have written the first draft of your "oo/oo" poem, the pair partners should read it quietly to themselves.

● Together you should discuss:

Which word combinations work well or sound best together?

Which word combinations sound weak and need to be revised in some way?

Should any changes be made in the order of the words on each line or in the order of the lines themselves?

● After you have made all your editing decisions, write the final draft of your "oo/oo" Poem in the space below in each of your activity texts.

Final Draft

1.

2.

3.

4.

5.

6.

7.

8.

Step Four

● When your team's final "oo/oo" Poem is complete, appoint one partner to read it to your class. What effect does the repeating "oo" sound in each team's poem have on its sound and meaning?

⑪

Place-Sounds Poem

Poets often use words in their poems that imitate the sounds they stand for, like "splash" and "boom." This technique is called **onomatopoeia**.

This exercise is a SMALL-GROUP activity. Before moving on to the instructions below, the class should break into small groups of four or five members.

One member of each group should act as scribe and write down all the team's ideas.

Step One

- The first step in writing a Place-Sounds Poem is to think of a busy place where many actions are going on and and where many sounds can be heard. An example is a crowded beach on a hot summer day.

- Group members should talk among themselves to decide on the place that their poem will describe.

- Next, in the space provided, the scribe should write a list of all the sounds members of the group can think of that might be heard at the place they have chosen. For example:

        Swimmers splashing
        Babies crying
        Seagulls squawking

- In trying to capture these place sounds on paper, each group should try to choose words that imitate those sounds as closely as possible. ("Children <u>dashing</u> over the hot sand" might be a better word choice than "children <u>running</u>"—since the "sh" sound in "dashing" sounds more like feet moving through sand.)

Place-Sounds List

_____

_____

_____

_____

_____

_____

_____

_____

_____

_____

_____

Step Two

- Each group should now take a look at its place-sounds list.

- Which phrases sound most like the actions they describe? Which phrases are most interesting to your ear? Which phrases seem to go together best?

- Which phrases don't seem to capture the sounds they are meant to describe? Can you think of better ways to express those sounds?

● Discuss which phrases the group would like to include in its Place-Sounds Poem. You must use at least eight sounds from your list.

● Finally, decide which order seems best. Then, the scribe should write your draft in the space below.

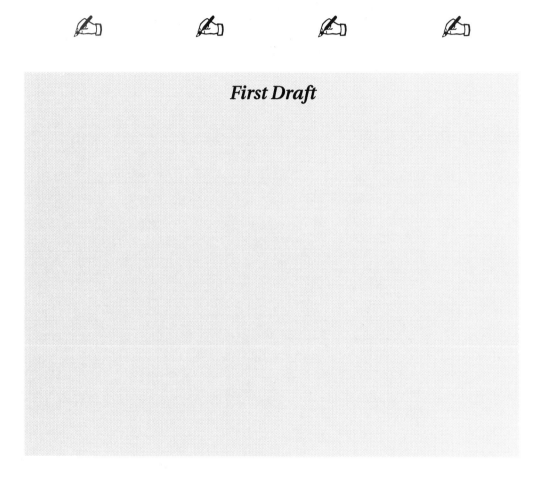

First Draft

Step Three

● When the first draft of each Place-Sounds Poem is complete, a member of each team should quietly read it aloud to the team.

● Can any group member suggest further changes to improve the poem? If so, the group should discuss the proposed changes and vote to see if they should be included.

● Then, members of your group should get together with members of one other group so you can read your drafts to each other.

● If members of the other group have suggestions for changes in your group's poem, discuss them and vote on whether to include them in your final draft.

● When all approved changes have been included, all students should write their group's final Place-Sounds Poem in the space below in each of their activity texts.

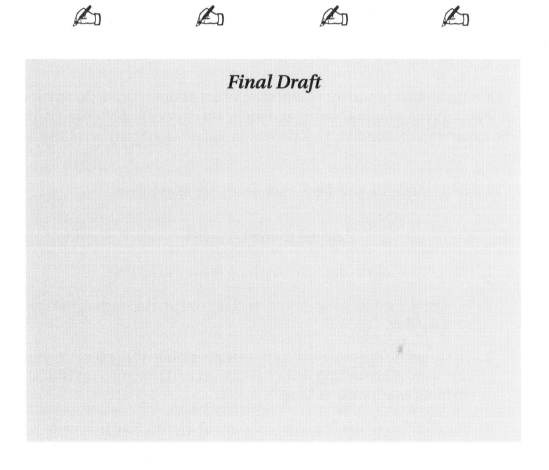

Final Draft

Step Four

● When each group's final Place-Sounds Poem is complete, a member of each group should read it aloud for the other groups. As a class, discuss which poems best capture the sounds of the places they describe.

12

Rhyme Mining

Although there are many types of poems that do not rhyme, poets often do make use of the technique of **rhyme**. For two words to rhyme they must share at least one identical final vowel sound—and a matching consonant sound, if they have one, as in "coat" and "boat."

This is a TEAM activity. The class should break into two equal teams and gather on opposite sides of the room.

One student is chosen (or volunteers) to act as both scribe (to write both teams' rhymes on the board) and judge (to check all challenged words in the classroom dictionary). This person therefore won't play on either team.

Two other students, one from each team, serve as timers.

How the Game Is Played

1. First, flip a coin to determine which team will go first.

2. To start the game, your teacher will say out loud a starter clue word, such as "dog."

3. The timer on the other team starts timing when the teacher says the clue word. The starting team has five seconds to come up with a rhyming word, such as "hog."

4. Any member of the team may shout out a word. The first word shouted out is considered the word in play.

5. If the first team does come up with an eligible rhyming word within five seconds, the scribe writes it on the board.

6. Now the opposing team has five seconds to come up with another rhyming word, such as "bog."

7. Play continues as long as each team keeps coming up with a legal rhyming word, which has not been previously used, within the five-second time limit.

How a Team Can Be Disqualified

Either team can be taken out of play for any of four reasons:

1. Not coming up with a new rhyming word within five seconds

2. Saying a word that has already been said

3. Offering a word that the judge rules does not actually rhyme with the starter word

4. Saying a word that does not appear in the judge's dictionary.

Once one team has been disqualified, members of the other team can continue listing rhymes on the board, with no more than five seconds between words, for as long as they can.

How the Game Is Scored

Teams receive one point for each rhyming word listed for them on the board.

A number of rounds, each with a new starter word, may be played.

The winning team is the one with the highest number of points at the end of play.

Rhyme Scheming

Very often poets will make use of rhyme in their poems in patterns called **rhyme schemes.** Using rhyme in set patterns this way can have powerful effects on a poem's sound and meaning.

This exercise is a PAIR activity calling for students to work in pairs.

Step One

- Many poems are patterns of lines that share a repeating scheme of rhyme and/or meter. (You'll learn about meter in a later section.) These patterns are called **stanzas.**

- One of the most common rhyme schemes is a four-line stanza in which the first and third lines rhyme and the second and fourth lines rhyme. Can you see why this pattern is called "A-B-A-B"?

```
Mary had a little lamb        A
Mary had some chocolate cake  B
Then a sandwich made of ham   A
Finally--a bellyache          B
```

- Notice that the rhyming words don't have to be spelled alike, they just have to sound alike ("ache" and "cake" are allowable rhymes).

- Each pair of partners should now work together to write three quick poems that use the "A-B-A-B" rhyme scheme.

- Work quickly and don't worry if your poems seem silly or don't make a great deal of sense. Just try to get the feel for this rhyme pattern.

- *Hint:* If you have trouble, try filling in the four rhyming end words first and then create lines to fit them.

● Partners should write their team's poems on their individual pages in the space below.

A-B-A-B Poems

No. 1

1.   **A**

2.   **B**

3.   **A**

4.   **B**

No. 2

1.   **A**

2.   **B**

3.   **A**

4.   **B**

No. 3

1.   **A**

2.   **B**

3.   **A**

4.   **B**

Step Two

● Another simple rhyme scheme to try is "A-B-B-A"—where the first and last lines rhyme and the two middle lines rhyme:

```
My favorite season is spring.      A
The cold winter breaks,             B
And new warmth awakes               B
A greenness in everything.          A
```

In the space provided, partners should now try writing three quick A-B-B-A poems.

A-B-B-A Poems

No. 1

1.   A

2.   B

3.   B

4.   A

No. 2

1.   A

2.   B

3.   B

4.   A

A-B-B-A Poems (continued)

No. 3

1.   **A**

2.   **B**

3.   **B**

4.   **A**

Step Three

● Now that each pair of partners has had a chance to explore the A-B-A-B and A-B-B-A rhyme schemes, try to use the schemes to compose a slightly longer rhyming poem.

● In the space below write an eight-line poem (two four-line stanzas) in which you use two A-B-A-B rhyme schemes, or two A-B-B-A rhyme schemes, or one of each pattern.

Final Rhyme-Scheme Poem

1.

2.

3.

4.

5.

6.

7.

8.

Step Four

● When your final poem is complete, have either partner share it with your class.

Then, have a class discussion about any difficulties you may have had working with rhyme schemes. Did working within a rhyme scheme make your task easier?

Syllable Poem

Another important way that poets make use of sound in their poems is in their use of **rhythm**. One useful rhythmic technique is to determine the number of **syllables** in each line.

This is a PAIR activity, calling for students to work in pairs.

Step One

● First, both partners in each pair should silently count the number of syllables in the sentence below:

```
I love hot dogs and hamburgers.
```

● Tell your partner how many syllables you counted.

● If you did not count eight, count **again**.

Step Two

● Now, each partner should write his or her own short warm-up sentence of at least eight words in the space that follows.

Warm-up Sentence

● When you have finished, exchange your sheet with your partner and count the number of syllables in each other's sentences.

● Do you agree on the number of syllables in both sentences? If so, you are both now ready to write a Syllable Poem.

Step Three

● In the space that follows you will see a pattern of six lines.

● In the ( ) after number 1, write in any number from 1 to 6—for example, 5.

● Quickly repeat this process of choosing random numbers for lines 2 through 6.

Random Numbers

1.   (   )

2.   (   )

3.   (   )

(continued)

Random Numbers (continued)

4.   (   )

5.   (   )

6.   (   )

Step Four

●   Now, you are ready to begin writing your Syllable Poem.

●   The numbers that you have put in the ( ) in each line represent the number of syllables that you will be allowed to use in that line.

●   For example, if you wrote "5" on line 1, you could write as your line: "I love my old dog" because that line has five syllables.

●   Now, work together with your partner to fill in the pattern with your own lines. Remember:

Each line can stand on its own

Or you can work to create a poem in which all the lines relate to a single theme or subject.

Step Five

●   When all students have completed Step Four, one partner of every pair should read the poems aloud for the rest of the class. First, read the random syllable numbers for each line (for example, "3-5-1-6-5-4"). Then, read the Syllable Poem composed to match this random pattern.

Can you begin to hear the effects of different syllable rhythms when they are combined in different ways?

Meeting Meter

Another way that poets use rhythm in their poems is through **meter.** Meter involves combining groups of stressed and unstressed syllables in set patterns to form varying poetic rhythms.

This exercise is a SMALL-GROUP activity for which the class should be divided into groups of three or four.

Step One

● Each meter pattern is a grouping of stressed and unstressed syllables.

The stressed syllables are marked: ´

The unstressed syllables are marked: ˘

● All students should say the following words quietly to themselves:

```
    happy        garage         criminal

      seventeen      enjoyable
```

● Now, still working individually, say each word again. In the space on the next page, mark the syllable that gets the most stress with a ´. For example:

```
        ´
      birthday
```

● Then mark the remaining syllables with a ˘:

```
        ´     ˘
      birthday
```

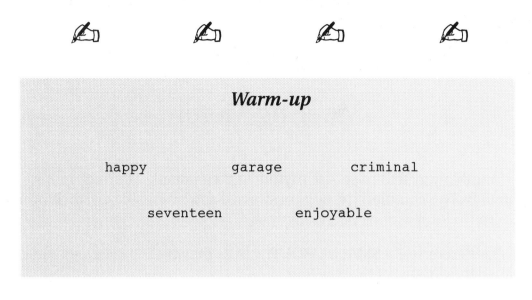

Warm-up

happy   garage   criminal

seventeen   enjoyable

Step Two

● Now, compare your markings with the markings of others in your group. Do you all agree? If not, talk about your answers until you do.

● Next, in the space that follows, each team should make a list of twenty two- or three-syllable words, such as "baseball" and "violet."

● When the group's list is complete, team members should work together to mark the stressed syllable in each word with a ′.

● Then they should mark the remaining syllables with a ˘.

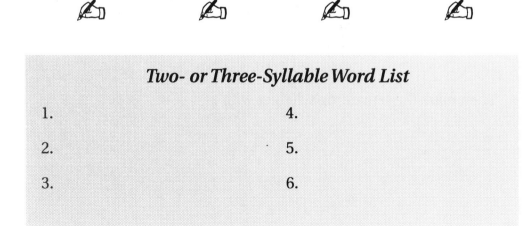

Two- or Three-Syllable Word List

1.   4.

2.   5.

3.   6.

Two- or Three-Syllable Word List (continued)

7.	14.
8.	15.
9.	16.
10.	17.
11.	18.
12.	19.
13.	20.

Step Three

In order to understand how to use meter, you must first get to know a few **meter patterns**. This activity will introduce six common ones:

Name	Stress Pattern	Example
1. **iamb** (I-am)	˘ ′	ĭn lóve
2. **trochee** (TRO-kee)	′ ˘	hún-grў
3. **anapest** (AN-a-pest)	˘ ˘ ′	ĭn ă rúsh
4. **dactyl** (DAK-til)	′ ˘ ˘	súd-dĕn-lў
5. **amphibrach** (AM-fa-brak)	˘ ′ ˘	ĭn-flá-tĭon
6. **spondee** (SPON-dee)	′ ′	Néw Yórk

⬤   Using the following space, members of each small group should now work together to think up three examples of the six meter patterns named above.

⬤   Your meter pattern examples can be either single words that fit the pattern, like "suddenly" and "inflation," or combinations of short words, like "in a rush" and "New York."

Meter Pattern Words or Phrases

1. Iamb ˘ ′	**4. Dactyl** ′ ˘ ˘
1.	1.
2.	2.
3.	3.
2. Trochee ′ ˘	**5. Amphibrach** ˘ ′ ˘
1.	1.
2.	2.
3.	3.
3. Anapest ˘ ˘ ′	**6. Spondee** ′ ′
1.	1.
2.	2.
3.	3.

Step Four

- When all groups are done, take time to compare your examples with those of the other groups. Do all of your examples belong with the meter name under which you have placed them?

- You are now ready to begin creating your Random-Meter Poem.

- First, in the following grid, write a random number from 1 to 6 under each line in the ( ) provided.

- When you are done, review the six meters introduced earlier in this activity. The number you have placed beneath each line will determine which of the six numbered meters you will use to fill out that piece of the grid. In other words, if you have marked (1) beneath, you will write in a word or phrase that is an iamb in the space above it.

- Now, fill in each of the nine blank lines in the grid with a word (or combination of words) that fits the meter that your random number has assigned to it.

- Don't try to make your Random-Meter Poem make sense. Just try to complete the grid as fast as you can.

- *Note:* You must use new words—not words from your own or other teams' warm-up lists.

Random-Meter Poem

_____   _____

(   )   (   )   (   )

(continued)

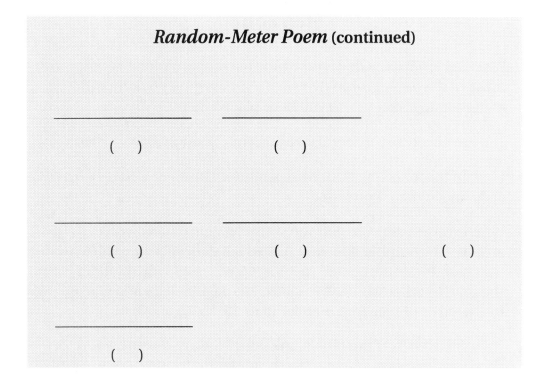

Step Five

● When each team is done, share your Random-Meter Poem with the rest of your class.

Can you hear the meter rhythms at work beneath the patterns of words that have been collected? Do certain meter combinations have special effects?

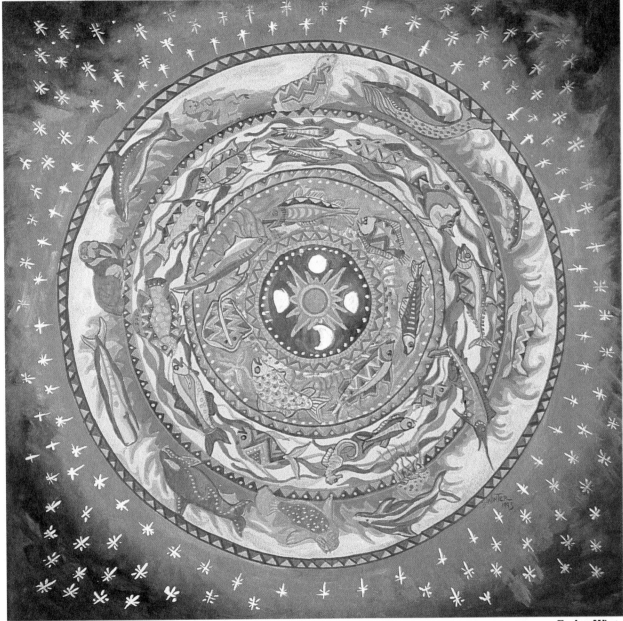

Poseidon's Dream   *Evelyn Winter*

III. POETRY DEVICES

16

Simile Poem

A **simile** is a poetic expression in which two elements are compared by using either "like" or "as." Examples include "She danced <u>like</u> a graceful swan" or "He had an appetite as big <u>as</u> Texas."

Step One

- The main function of the device of the simile is to allow the poet to make comparisons:

      The sound of the ocean <u>was</u> like a lion roaring.

      The smell of a rose is as sweet <u>as</u> a mountain
      breeze in spring.

- One of the most interesting aspects of the simile is its ability to tie together two ideas that at first don't seem to belong together:

      My life is <u>like</u> a speeding convertible on a
      deadly winding highway.

      His smile was as bright <u>as</u> a two-ton explosion of
      TNT.

- In the space on the next page, make a list of as many similes as possible to accompany the starter word "blue," which must appear somewhere in every line.

  Use both the simile form that uses "like" ("Blue <u>like</u> a summer sky") and the form that uses "as" ("As blue <u>as</u> a rainy day without a friend").

Try to be as creative as possible. Make use of the simile's ability to join ideas that don't seem at first to fit together.

Also, work as fast as you can and write down every idea that occurs to you, even if it doesn't seem worth recording.

Simile List

Simile List (continued)

Step Two

- Now, take a moment to review your simile list.

- Which ones are most interesting? Which ones sound best?

- Do some of your similes seem as if they might work well together as a Simile Poem?

- Choose the simile lines that you would like to use. Any number of lines is acceptable.

- Then, decide on the order in which they should appear and write them in the following space.

First Draft

(continued)

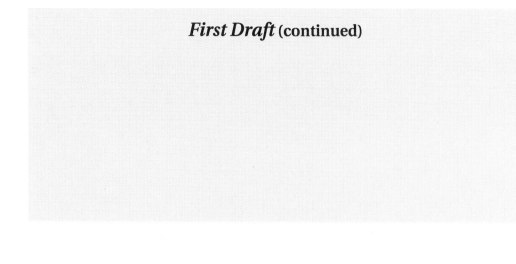

First Draft (continued)

Step Three

● Now look at the rough draft of your Simile Poem.

● Do any similes seem weaker than the rest? Can you think of ways to improve them or replace them with stronger ones?

● Does the order of your similes seem right? Should any lines be switched around to make the poem more effective?

● When you have finished making all necessary changes, copy the final draft of your Simile Poem in the following space.

Final Draft

Final Draft (continued)

Step Four

● When your final Simile Poem is complete, share it with your class. How did other class members combine similes to make a poem? What were the most memorable similes for "blue"?

Making Metaphors

Like a simile, a **metaphor** involves a comparison between two items that are essentially unlike. However, the metaphor eliminates the connector "like" or "as" and makes the comparison directly.

SIMILE: The moon is <u>like</u> a cheese pizza.

METAPHOR: The moon <u>is</u> a cheese pizza.

This exercise is a SMALL-GROUP activity, calling for the class to be divided into groups of three or four.

Step One

● Like similes, metaphors have the potential to stretch the reader's imagination by joining items that are quite unlike.

● As a warm-up, each small-group member should write five additional Moon Metaphors similar to the example on the previous page.

Be as creative as you can.

To create strong metaphors, explore various aspects of the moon by comparing it with unexpected objects or ideas. For example:

```
The moon is a Frisbee that glows in the dark.

The moon is the first step on the stairway to
infinity.
```

Moon Metaphors

1.

2.

3.

4.

5.

Step Two

● When each group member has completed five moon metaphors, take a few moments to share them with other members of your group.

● Discuss which metaphors seem to work best. Can you figure out why?

● Now that you are a little more familiar with making metaphors, move on to creating a group Animal-Metaphor Poem.

● Choose one group member to act as scribe and write down the group's ideas.

● Then as a group, in the space that follows, brainstorm a list of twenty metaphors, each of which includes a comparison of someone or something with a different animal, as in "My baby brother is a <u>pig</u> when he eats" and "The stars are a litter of <u>kittens</u> that never grow up."

● Work fast and don't hold back any ideas—even if they seem "crazy." Let yourselves be as imaginative as possible.

Animal-Metaphor List

1.

2.

3.

4.

5.

6.

7.

8.

(continued)

Animal-Metaphor List (continued)

9.

10.

11.

12.

13.

14.

15.

16.

17.

18.

19.

20.

Step Three

● As a group, review the animal metaphors you have listed above in order to create your group Animal-Metaphor Poem.

Which metaphors work most effectively?

Can you see ways to improve some of the metaphors?

Can you think of new metaphors to substitute for the weaker ones?

When you are ready, begin to create your Animal-Metaphor Poem in the space below. Write your best lines in the order that seems appropriate to you.

You may use any number of metaphors that help to create the strongest poem.

If possible, choose animal metaphors that seem to belong together in some way, even if the logic appears surprising at first.

First Draft

Step Four

- Have one member of your group read the first draft of your Animal-Metaphor Poem aloud.

- Does any member of the group have any suggested changes?

    Do the wording and rhythm of each line sound as strong as they could be?

    Does the order of the lines seem right?

- When the group has agreed on all necessary changes, each member should write the group's final draft in the following space.

Final Draft

Final Draft (continued)

Step Five

● When all Animal-Metaphor Poems are complete, members of each group should read the poems to the class. After hearing them all, which animal metaphors stick in your mind? Can you explain why?

18

Denotation and Connotation

The very foundation of many poems rests on the fact that words can perform more than one function at the same time.

The literal meaning (dictionary definition) of a word is called its **denotation**. The denotation of the word "flag" might be "a piece of fabric of distinctive design often used as the symbol of a nation."

The **connotations** of a word are all the poetic meanings it suggests beyond its literal meaning. Connotations for "flag" might be "patriotism," "war," or "community."

Generally, denotations are straightforward and factual, while connotations evoke strong feelings.

This exercise is a PAIR activity, calling for students to work in pairs.

Step One

- In the following space, you will find five separate words, each printed twice.

- After each word with a "D" in front of it, work with your partner to write its denotative meaning. (You shouldn't need to use a dictionary; explain the meaning as well as you can.) For example: **D** Spring: "The season of the year after winter and before summer."

- After each word with a "C" in front of it, write some of its **connotative** (poetic) meanings. For example, **C** Spring: "greenness; warmth; rebirth."

Denotations and Connotations

D 1.   **Night:**

C 1.   **Night:**

D 2.   **Sun:**

C 2.   **Sun:**

D 3.   **Storm:**

C 3.   **Storm:**

Denotations and Connotations (continued)

D 4.   **Mother:**

C 4.   **Mother:**

D 5.   **Heart:**

C 5.   **Heart:**

Step Two

● When you and your partner have completed the previous step, share your answers with other teams in your class.

   Were all the denotative definitions for each of the five words basically the same?

   How many different connotations did the class come up with for each of the words?

● Now that you are more experienced in distinguishing between denotations and connotations, each partner can move on to writing his or her own Object Poem.

● First, think of an object in your own life that creates strong feelings in you—either positive or negative (a souvenir from a trip, a special photograph, or an article of clothing).

● In Column I, list all its denotative qualities. This list should be very descriptive. If your object is a ring, for example, tell about its size, shape, color, and history—how you got it and when you almost lost it.

● In Column II, list some of its connotative qualities—the feelings it creates in you and its special meanings to you. For example: "The ring's red stone reminds me of the heart of my grandmother who gave it to me," and "The tarnish on the ring reminds me that nothing ever stays the same."

● Try to fill up both columns with an equal number of entries.

Object Poem Brainstorm

Name of object: _____

Column I   **Column II**

_____

_____

_____

_____

_____

_____

_____

_____

_____

_____

_____

Step Three

● When your Object Poem brainstorming is complete, it's time to work your ideas into a poem.

● Start by creating a line for your poem out of either column. An example could be: "The ring is very worn—it must be old."

● Then, try to make a line from an entry in the opposite column, such as "If this ring could speak, what wisdom could it share with me?"

● Proceed in this way, alternating between entries from each column, until you feel the poem is complete. Your finished poem may be as long as you wish, but it must contain at least ten lines.

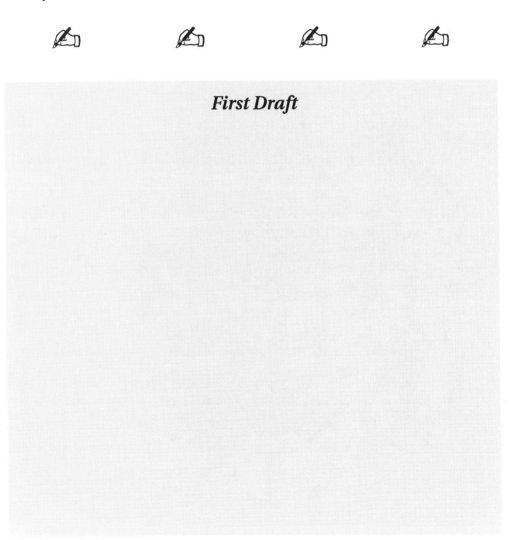

First Draft

Step Four

- As soon as the Object Poem drafts are complete, partners should exchange them.

- When each of you has had a chance to read the other's poem, share your reactions.

    First, tell all the things you like about your partner's poem:

    > Images or feelings that seem particularly striking

    > Words that seem well chosen

    > Effective use of rhythm and other sound devices

    Then, share (in a respectful way) your reactions to things that do not seem as strong to you:

    > Images or feelings that seem exaggerated or unrealistic

    > Words that seem weak or poorly used

    > Ways that rhythm or other sound devices are not used as effectively as they might be

    When you have finished critiquing each other's works, take time to read your own draft quietly to yourself.

- Make any changes that you wish to make and copy your final draft in the following space.

Final Draft

Final Draft (continued)

Step Five

● When you have completed the final draft of your Object Poem, share it with your class. Did all your classmates' poems capture the powerful mixture of denotations and connotations?

⑲

Understanding Symbols

One important way that poets make use of denotation and connotation in their poems is with **symbols.** A symbol is a sign or object that, in addition to itself, suggests some other meaning, often an idea or feeling. For example, a "tree" in a poem could also stand for "life," and a "snake" might also stand for "evil."

Step One

● In the exercise that follows, the objects in Column I might be used to symbolize the ideas or feelings in Column II.

● Place the matching letter from Column II in the space in front of the correct object in Column I.

Symbols Matching Exercise

Column I	Column II
1. butterfly	A. royalty
2. rose	B. light
3. skull	C. marriage
4. lion	D. romance
5. black cat	E. growth and change
6. sun	F. bad luck
7. crown	G. fierceness
8. two intersecting rings	H. death

Step Two

- When you have finished, compare your answers with those of your classmates. Did any students disagree on how to match up the items? Can they defend the alternate choices they made?

- Now, you are ready to move on to write your own Symbol Poem.

- Your poem will center around one symbol of your own choosing. It should be an object that can easily stand for another idea (or ideas) in addition to itself.

  You may use one of the symbols listed in the preceding warm-up exercise

  Or, you may choose one of the traditional symbols listed here:

hourglass *or* clock	book
snake	ship
clown	mountain
night	gun
moon *or* stars	wall
ball	pen

  Or, you may choose a symbol of your own.

- Once you have chosen the symbol (for example, "ball"), write it on the first line of the Symbol Poem grid that follows.

- Then, compose four more lines to flesh out the poem, strictly following the structure of this model:

  ```
  Ball
  Round and proud
  You remind me of this lonely earth
  Spinning alone in space
  I wish I did not have to spin so alone.
  ```

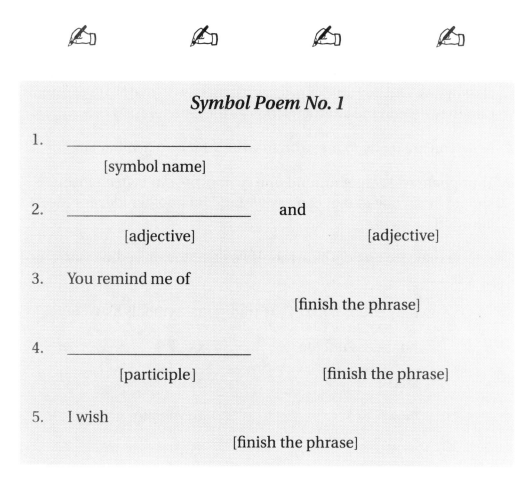

Symbol Poem No. 1

1. _____

   [symbol name]

2. _____   and

   [adjective]   [adjective]

3. You remind me of

                              [finish the phrase]

4. _____

   [participle]   [finish the phrase]

5. I wish

                 [finish the phrase]

Step Three

● When your Symbol Poem is complete, share it with your class. How did other class members use symbols to make a poem?

● Using the same instructions as in Step Two, choose another symbol and write a second Symbol Poem in the space that follows.

Symbol Poem No. 2

1. _____
   [symbol name]

2. _____ and
   [adjective]   [adjective]

3. You remind me of

   [finish the phrase]

4. _____
   [participle]   [finish the phrase]

5. I wish

   [finish the phrase]

Step Four

● Now, compare your two Symbol Poems. How do they make use of the actual qualities of the symbol objects to express wider ideas?

Do you think one of your Symbol Poems is more successful than the other? Can you explain why?

Personification

The poetic device of **personification** is a special kind of metaphor. It involves giving human characteristics to nonhuman subjects, such as animals, objects, or even ideas. Here's an example: "On summer nights, the moon <u>smiles</u> on everyone in love."

This exercise is a PAIR activity, calling for students to work in pairs.

Step One

- First, you and your partner should read through the following list of animals, objects, and ideas.

- For each subject, work together to write a short phrase that uses personification to give the subject a human quality.

  The personification can be created by a verb that suggests a human action: "The sun <u>sang</u> a happy tune on our wedding day."

  Or, the personification can be created by using a participle: "The ducks crossed the highway, <u>marching</u> in perfect parade order."

  Or, the personification can be created by using a simile: "When love touches your heart, it feels <u>like a violin being played inside</u>."

- In each of your phrases, underline the words that create the personification.

Personification Warm-up

1. **cat:**

2. **eagle:**

3. **elephant:**

4. **star:**

5. **tulip:**

6. **raindrop:**

7. **wish:**

8. **fear:**

9. **love:**

Step Two

- Share your team's Personification Warm-up phrases with the rest of your class. Discuss which phrases work best. Can you explain why?

- Now you and your partner are ready to write a five-line Personification Poem together.

- Choose an animal, object, or idea that you believe has many human characteristics to explore. Examples might include a puppy, an old car, or loneliness.

● At the top of a column write your subject. Then make a brainstorm list of all the human characteristics you can match with it. For example:

JOY

--<u>can't</u> <u>sit</u> still
--<u>whistles</u> night and day
--<u>grins</u> the broadest grin
--even <u>hugs</u> strangers. . . .

● When you have completed your list, talk with your partner and choose the five best entries.

● Then write them in the space below in the order that seems best.

First Draft

1.

2.

3.

4.

5.

Step Three

● When the draft of your Personification Poem is complete, read it quietly to yourself.

Which lines sound strongest?

Do any words or images need to be revised?

Do any new ideas occur to you that should be included?

● Make all necessary changes on your draft. Then write your final draft in the space below.

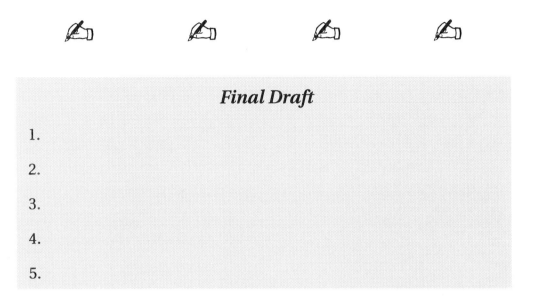

Final Draft

1.

2.

3.

4.

5.

Step Four

● When your final Personification Poem is complete, share it with your class. How did other class writers use personification to compose their poems?

Astral Lizards   *Evelyn Winter*

IV. POEM PATTERNS AND SHAPES

Haiku

Many poets turn to traditional poetic forms when setting out to write a poem. Working within established poetic structures can often help shape their ideas.

The **haiku** (hi-KOO) is a three-line Japanese verse form. Its first line has five syllables; its second line has seven syllables; its third line has five syllables. The lines of a haiku do not rhyme.

A haiku often involves images from nature. Also, the last line sometimes contains an element of surprise, an unexpected twist on the first two lines:

```
Crows caw at evening
Black cats screech and prowl below--
Dinnertime for all.
```

Step One

● First, on the next page, practice writing lines of five and seven syllables.

● Try to make all of your lines contain images from nature. Here are some examples:

Five syllables: `Ghost fog, white and wet`

Seven syllables: `Shining summer lake at noon`

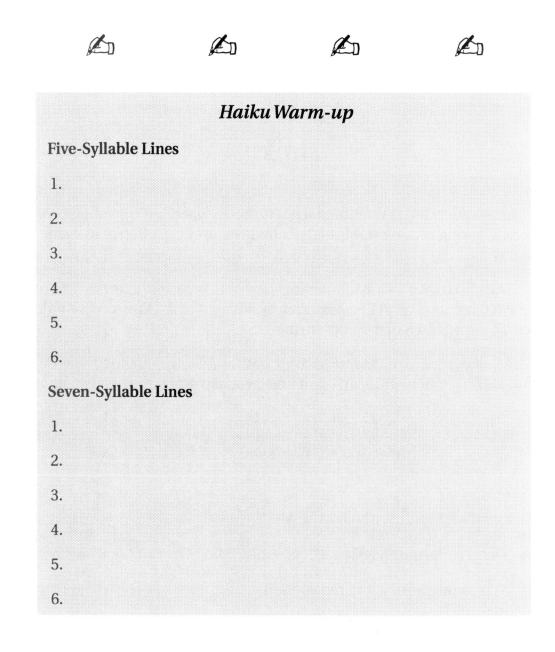

Haiku Warm-up

Five-Syllable Lines

1.

2.

3.

4.

5.

6.

Seven-Syllable Lines

1.

2.

3.

4.

5.

6.

Step Two

● Take a look at the lines you have written. Have you counted the syllables in each line correctly? Which lines are most interesting? Which
lines sound best to your ear?

● Now, it's time to write three finished haiku in the space that follows.

   You may use any of the lines you have composed above

   Or you may write new lines.

● Remember to use images from nature, and try to work in an unexpected twist in the third line.

First Draft

Haiku No. 1

1.

2.

3.

Haiku No. 2

1.

2.

3.

Haiku No. 3

1.

2.

3.

Step Three

● Now, read each complete haiku quietly to yourself.

How do the rhythms of the three lines of each haiku work together? Should you change the words or the order of the words in any line?

How does the combination of consonants and vowels in each line sound to your ear? Should you make any changes?

How does the logic of the three lines work together? Do they create a picture? Do they make a statement?

Does the third line contain a surprise?

● Make any changes that you think necessary. Then copy your completed haiku in the following spaces.

Final Draft

Haiku No. 1

1.

2.

3.

Haiku No. 2

1.

2.

3.

Final Draft (continued)

Haiku No. 3

1.

2.

3.

Step Four

● Choose your favorite finished haiku and share it with your class. Which class haiku worked best? Can you explain why?

22

Cinquain

The **cinquain** (SIN-kane) poetic form has five lines that do not rhyme. Like the haiku, it involves counting a set number of syllables for each line— 2 / 4 / 6 / 8 / and 2:

```
            Cinquain

        Subway
        Posters slipping
        Backwards into the dark
        Under the ground as the sleek train
        Speeds by.
```

Step One

● Think of a subject, like the subway train above, that you would like to write about in the cinquain form.

● In the five-line grids that follow, try different ways of sketching out your idea.

● Two ways to make your cinquain stronger are to:

   1. Avoid too many adjectives—as in "wide, salty, rough ocean"

   2. Cluster several nouns like "ocean sand seagull surf"

● Another way to make your cinquain sound more interesting is to let some of your lines spill over into the next line. In poetry, this is called a **run-on** line. Notice how this is done in the subway cinquain: Subway / Posters slipping / Backwards into the dark / Under the ground . . .

● Also, like the haiku, the cinquain's short final line can hold some surprises:

Either by summing up the whole poem, as in "Speeds by"

Or by contrasting with earlier ideas in the poem:

```
She smiles
That perfect grin,
Those eyes so twinkling bright,
In love all right! But now in love--
With him . . .
```

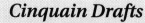

Cinquain Drafts

Version No. 1

   1.

   2.

   3.

   4.

   5.

Cinquain Drafts (continued)

Version No. 2

1.

2.

3.

4.

5.

Version No. 3

1.

2.

3.

4.

5.

Step Two

- Now, read your best cinquain draft quietly to yourself.

- Which lines sound strongest? Could any words, lines, or images be improved?

- Have you followed the writing suggestions offered in Step One?

- When you have made all your final revisions, write your final draft on the following page.

Final Draft

1.

2.

3.

4.

5.

Step Three

● When your final cinquain is complete, share it with your class. How did other class members make use of this fixed form of poetry?

Did having to work within the requirements of the cinquain form make writing the poem easier or more difficult?

Concrete Poetry

Concrete poetry is a special type of "visual" poetry. In concrete poetry, the poet's choice about how to set the words on the page plays a very important part in the poem. The poem's *shape* reflects its message.

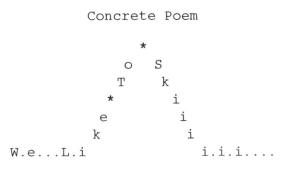

This exercise is a PAIR activity, calling for students to work in pairs.

Step One

- To compose your own concrete poem, you and your partner can begin in one of two ways.

- One method is to think of the content of your poem first: What is the poem going to be about? What words will it include?

  Then, think about how to create a suitable poem-picture on the page. For example, first you decide to compose a concrete poem with the words "Love is forever" in it; then you decide on a shape to fit the message.

- The opposite method is first to visualize a poem-picture on the page. What shape will it take? What message will it suggest?

  Then, you compose the words that will best suit the picture. For example you decide to create a concrete poem in the shape of two interlocking circles; then you choose the words to include and decide how to include them.

- Starting with one of these methods, each pair of students should work together to create the first draft of their concrete poem. Then each partner should copy that draft in the space on the next page in their activity texts.

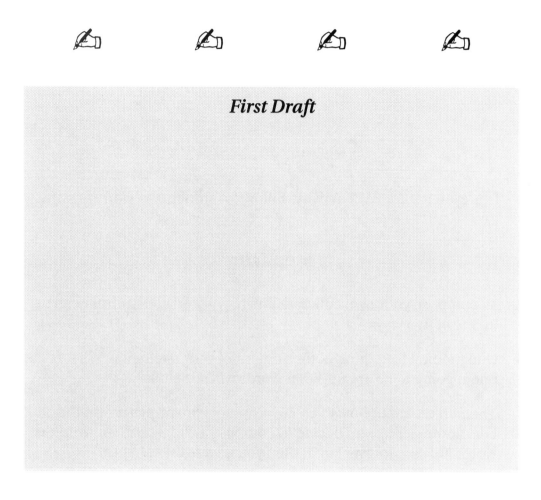

First Draft

Step Two

- When you and your partner have completed your concrete poem draft, take a moment to look it over.

- Do you see any improvements you could make?

  Should you make any changes in the words you chose?

  Should you make any changes in the poem-picture you created?

  Can you see any ways to make the overall message of the poem more effective?

- After you have discussed all possible changes with your partner, exchange drafts with one other pair of students.

● Can the two teams offer each other any helpful suggestions to improve the concrete poems?

● Now, make your final changes and copy your final draft in the following space.

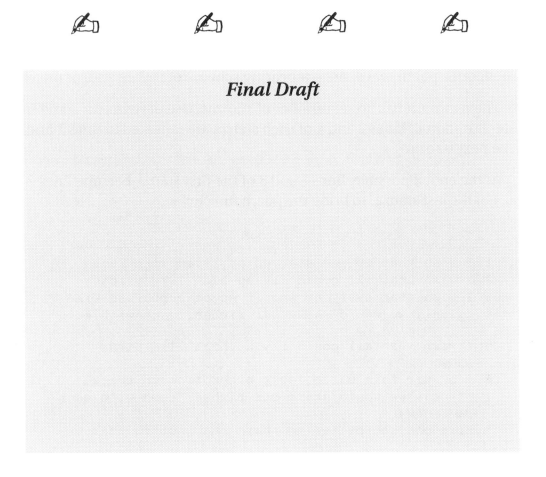

Step Three

● When your concrete poem is complete, share it with the class. How did other teams use this poetic technique to express their ideas?

24

Pantoum

The poetic form of the **pantoum** is made up of **stanzas** of four lines each that are linked in an interesting way. (A stanza is a pattern of lines throughout a poem that share a repeating scheme of rhyme and/or meter.)

The pantoum has no set number of stanzas. Use of rhyme or standard meter is optional. Lines 2 and 4 of each stanza are repeated in lines 1 and 3 of the next stanza.

At the end, if possible, lines 1 and 3 of the first stanza become lines 2 and 4 of the last stanza, to bring the poem full circle.

Pantoum

```
 1. I wish that no one starved or lived with rats
 2. I wish that all could fly up high like birds
 3. I wish that everyone who lived on earth was free
 4. If only we would share our riches, each with each

 5. I wish that all could fly up high like birds
    [same as line 2]
 6. I'm sure this earth looks nicer from up there
 7. If only we would share our riches, each with each
    [same as line 4]
 8. More blessed by far to share than not to share.

 9. I'm sure this earth looks nicer from up there
    [same as line 6]
10. Yet those who wait in need are still down here
11. More blessed by far to share than not to share
    [same as line 8]
12. More hope of helping here than flying higher

13. Yet those who wait in need are still down here
    [same as line 10]
14. I wish that no one starved or lived with rats
    [same as line 1]
15. More hope of helping here than flying higher
    [same as line 12]
16. I wish that everyone who lived on earth was free.
    [same as line 3]
```

Step One

● Try writing your own pantoum, based on the outline that follows.

● Remember, you don't have to use rhyme or standard meter—but you may if you wish.

● Pay attention to the patterns of sound and meaning that occur as lines repeat throughout your poem.

First Draft

1.

2.

3.

4.

5.   [same as line 2]

6.

7.   [same as line 4]

8.

9.   [same as line 6]

10.

11.   [same as line 8]

12.

(continued)

First Draft (continued)

13.   [same as line 10]

14.   [same as line 1]

15.   [same as line 12]

16.   [same as line 3]

Step Two

- Read the first draft of your pantoum quietly to yourself.

- Does the repetition of the interlocking lines in the poem suggest interesting meanings?

- Can you see changes to make in specific lines, or in the order of the lines, that would strengthen the poem?

- Make all helpful changes and copy your final draft in the following space.

Final Draft

1.

2.

3.

4.

5.   [same as line 2]

6.

Final Draft (continued)

7.   [same as line 4]

8.

9.   [same as line 6]

10.

11.   [same as line 8]

12.

13.   [same as line 10]

14.   [same as line 1]

15.   [same as line 12]

16.   [same as line 3]

Step Three

● When you have completed the final draft of your pantoum, share it with your class. How did other classmates make use of this poem form's special repeating-lines feature?

Blue Moon

Evelyn Winter

V. PUTTING IT ALL TOGETHER

Free Verse

Free verse is poetry that is written without any regular meter or rhyme scheme. Since the flow of free verse springs from the poem's own thoughts and feelings, the length of each line and the number of lines in each stanza varies.

```
              The air is cold.

The endless rolling surf
crashes
on the wintry beach.

I see my breath
  in every breath--
missing you more and more
                    with each
          receding
      wave.
```

Step One

- Before you go further with this activity, take a moment to study the sample poem above.

- If you compare it with stricter poem forms, you should notice a few important differences.

    First, the poem has no regular rhyme scheme.

    Second, the poem has no strict meter.

    Third, the poem's lines are many lengths and seem to be placed on the page very freely to fit their specific content.

● These are some of the reasons why this poetic technique is called "free" verse!

● To write a Landscape-Contrast Poem in free verse, first choose an outdoor place to write about that is meaningful to you (a special place near your home, a place that you visited on vacation, or a place that you read about in a book).

● The aim of your poem is to use free verse to describe the place at two contrasting times, such as two different times of day or two different seasons.

● Write from your "heart." Use specific details to express thoughts and feelings. (Your poem should be at least twelve lines—but it can be longer.)

● Also, feel free to use poetic techniques that you have already learned about—alliteration, assonance, rhyme, rhythm, similes, metaphors, symbols, personification—to bring your poem to life.

● Finally, be sure to think about how you will use the freedom to vary line length and placement on the page.

First Draft

First Draft (continued)

Step Two

- Now, quietly read your first draft to yourself.

- Which lines sound best? Which lines sound weakest? Can you tell why? What changes can you make?

- Do any lines seem weak because they sound false or untrue? How can you improve them?

- Consider the length of your lines and how you have placed them on the page. Does this placement fit the mood and feeling of each line?

- Make all changes necessary to improve your poem. Then write your final draft in the following space.

Final Draft

Step Three

- When your final Landscape-Contrast Poem is complete, share it with your class. What choices did other class members make to take advantage of the freedom of free verse?

"*X* Ways of Looking at . . ." Poem

One of America's most respected modern poets, Wallace Stevens, wrote a well-known poem called "Thirteen Ways of Looking at a Blackbird." In that poem each stanza looks at the central image of a blackbird in surprisingly different ways.

This activity asks you to create your own "*X* Ways of Looking at . . ." Poem in free verse. You will choose your own central repeating image.

This exercise is a PAIR activity, calling for students to work in pairs.

Step One

- First, listen carefully as your teacher reads the first five stanzas of Wallace Stevens's poem "Thirteen Ways of Looking at a Blackbird."

- Make sure to have a dictionary handy to look up any words that you do not understand.

- Notice how differently Stevens sees and describes the blackbird in each stanza.

- Now, consult with your partner to pick a subject for your own "*X* Ways of Looking at . . ." Poem. What subject could you choose to look at from a variety of ways?

● When you have chosen your subject, take time to list in the following space as many different ways as possible to look at it.

Subject Brainstorm List

Step Two

● Take a look at your list. Discuss with your partner which entries you might want to include in your "*X* Ways of Looking at . . ." Poem. Put a check mark next to those entries.

● Now, begin to compose separate stanzas for each important idea. (You must have at least five stanzas and no more than thirteen.)

● Some important decisions you will have to make are:

1. How many lines to have in each stanza

2. How long each line should be

3. How many stanzas to include

4. What order to place the stanzas in

● When you are ready, write the rough draft of your "*X* Ways of Looking at . . ." Poem in the following space.

● For your poem's title, count the number of stanzas in your draft and substitute this number for the *X*. Then fill in the name of your subject after "Looking at _____" (for example, "<u>Ten</u> Ways of Looking at <u>Hot</u> <u>Dogs</u>").

First Draft

(continued)

First Draft (continued)

Step Three

● When you and your partner have completed the first draft, take time to read it quietly to yourselves.

● How does the poem read as a whole? Does the order of stanzas make sense? Do the lines in each stanza sound good together?

Can you think of changes that would improve the poem? Make them and then copy your final draft in the following space.

Final Draft

Step Four

● When you have completed the final draft of your "*X* Ways of Looking at . . ." Poem, share it with your class. In what ways did classmates draw inspiration from this well-known poem model?

Scribble Poem

Poets get ideas for their poems from many different sources—personal memories, daily happenings in their lives, current events, and so forth. But sometimes they get stuck and can't think of anything to write about.

One way to get unstuck is the scribble poem, a form of free-writing poetry that helps you tap into poem ideas that you didn't even know were in you.

Step One

● The first step is easy: Just relax . . . close your eyes . . . take a few slow, easy breaths . . . take time to let your mind and body enjoy being completely quiet.

● The next step is to make the scribble that your poem will be based upon. (Have a pencil ready.)

● Before you make your scribble, read through the following steps completely:

First, close your eyes and poise your pencil anywhere above the blank space on the next page.

Lowering the pencil to the page, quickly—without thinking—let your pencil point draw a scribble.

Your scribble can be simple or complicated, relaxed or full of emotion—all depending on what feelings you let your pencil express.

When you are ready, follow these steps to draw your scribble in the space below.

Scribble

Step Two

● Now, look at your scribble. What do you see?

● Keep looking at it in new and fresh ways. Does it suggest poem ideas?

● Describe it: its shape, its size, its placement on the page. (You might say "The small figure in the corner of the page reminds me of how it feels to be an outsider.")

● Invent similes: It looks like . . . sounds like . . . feels like . . . smells like . . . tastes like . . . ("It looks like a banana. Maybe I could write a funny poem about someone slipping on a banana peel.")

● Ask: If this scribble had feelings, they probably would be . . . ("The scribble line looks dark and full of anger. Do I have angry feelings today that I might write about in a poem?")

If I had to give this scribble a name, I would call it . . . ("Because my scribble looks like a smile, I will start a poem called 'Mona Lisa' and see what comes up.")

If this scribble holds a secret, it might be . . . ("The scribble is very twisty, probably not to be trusted. Could I find ways to write about the theme of 'trust' in my life?")

● If you run out of ideas to list, you can divide your scribble in half, or thirds, or quarters. Then repeat the steps above, studying each part as if it were a new scribble all by itself.

● You may choose to use any or none of these approaches. The important thing is to keep looking at your scribble and to write in the following space every idea that comes to you.

Scribble Brainstorm

Scribble Brainstorm (continued)

Step Three

- Now, take a few minutes to review your list.

- Put a star beside each entry that piques your interest—for any reason. (Perhaps it's an interesting idea, or it has a nice sound, or it provokes a strong feeling.)

- When you're done, pick one of your starred items (or any combination of them) to act as a poem starter.

- In the following space, write the first draft of a poem, using your poem starter and any poetic form you have learned in past activities.

First Draft

(continued)

First Draft (continued)

Step Four

- When you have finished the first draft of your scribble poem, quietly read it to yourself.

- Make any revisions necessary to improve it. Then write the final draft in the following space.

- If you wish, give your final poem a title.

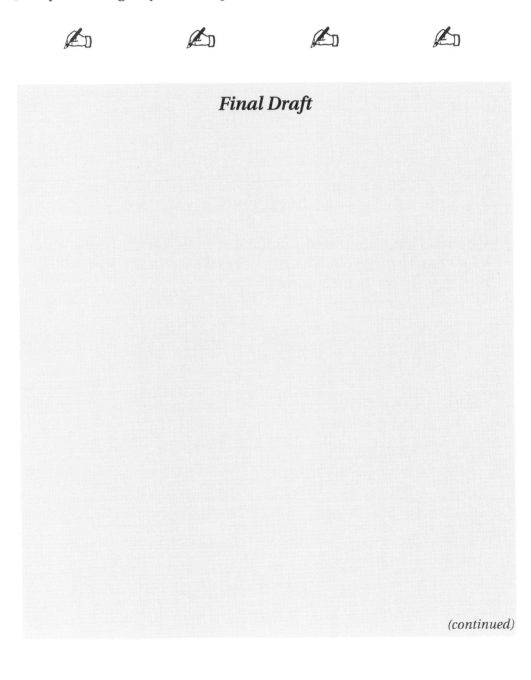

Final Draft

(continued)

Final Draft (continued)

Step Five

● When you have completed your final scribble poem, share it with your class. How did other classmates make use of this free-writing technique to create their poems?

Glossary

These pages provide a complete glossary of the major poetic terms introduced throughout the preceding poetry-writing activities.

First, take a few minutes to read slowly through the list. Of all the terms that you have studied, how many do you recognize? How many of the terms could you define in your own words without looking at the definition?

Next, make a note of any terms that you still may not fully understand. Go back through your activity text to review those concepts.

concrete poetry—A type of poetry in which the shape of the poem as it is set on the page reflects the content of the poem

connotation—The poetic meaning associated with a word in addition to its literal meaning (flag = "patriotism," "war," "community")

consonance—Repetition of consonant sounds, especially in the middle or at the end of words ("Ea*s*y day*s* of lei*s*ure in the gra*ss*")

couplet—A pair of rhymed lines, often occurring at the end of a poem

denotation—The literal meaning (dictionary definition) of a word (flag: "a piece of fabric of distinctive design often used as the symbol of a nation")

dramatic monologue—A poetic form in which poets speak in the voice of a character other than themselves

free verse—A poem without any regular meter or rhyme scheme, in which the length of each line and the number of lines in each stanza often varies

haiku—A three-line Japanese verse form with five syllables in its first line, seven syllables in its second line, and five syllables in its third line

metaphor—A direct poetic comparison, without the use of "like" or "as," between two items that are essentially unlike ("The moon *is* a cheese pizza")

meter—Combining groups of stressed and unstressed syllables in set patterns to form varying poetic rhythms, with the six most common:

Name	Stress Pattern	Example
iamb (I-am)	˘ ′	ĭn lóve
trochee (TRO-kee)	′ ˘	hún-grў
anapest (AN-a-pest)	˘ ˘ ′	ĭn ă rúsh
dactyl (DAK-til)	′ ˘ ˘	súd-dĕn-lў
amphibrach (AM-fa-brak)	˘ ′ ˘	ĭn-flá-tĭon
spondee (SPON-dee)	′ ′	Néw Yórk

onomatopoeia—The effect created by words (or whole lines) that imitate the sounds they stand for ("splash" or "boom")

pantoum—A poem form with any number of four-line stanzas, in which the second and fourth lines of each stanza become the first and third lines of the following stanza.

personification—A poetic device that involves giving human characteristics to nonhuman subjects such as animals, objects, and even ideas ("On summer nights the moon <u>smiles</u> on everyone in love")

prose—Words written in sentence form without rhyme or fixed meter

prose poem—A poem form that looks like prose on the page, but sounds like poetry when read aloud

rhyme—The effect achieved when words share at least one identical final vowel sound and matching consonant sound if they have one, but the consonant before the vowel need not be matching ("<u>coat</u>" and "<u>boat</u>")

rhyme scheme—The pattern of rhymes used in a poem, most often at the end of each line (A-B-A-B)

rhythm—the ordered, recurrent alternation of strong and weak elements in the flow of sound and silence in speech

run-on line—A line with no final punctuation (or other call for a pause) that runs on into the following line

```
Running and running I fell
Into a hole as deep as a well . . .
```

simile—A poetic expression in which two elements are compared by using either "like" or "as" ("She danced like a graceful swan" or "He had an appetite as big as Texas")

sonnet—A fourteen-line poem form most often written in iambic pentameter (five metrical feet of one unstressed and one stressed syllable each) with a variety of possible rhyme schemes, including Shakespearean (ABAB/CDCD/EFEF/GG) and Italian (ABBAABBA/CDECDE)

stanza—A pattern of lines throughout a poem that share a repeating scheme of rhyme and/or meter

symbol—A sign or object that in addition to itself suggests some other meaning, often an idea or feeling (A "tree" in a poem can also stand for "life" or a "snake" can stand for "evil")

syllable—Any word or part of a word pronounced with a single, uninterrupted sounding of the voice ("Ba-nan-a"—three syllables)

terza rima—A poetic form made up of any number of three-line stanzas, usually written in iambic pentameter, with the first and third lines of each stanza rhyming and the second line in rhyme with the first and third lines of the next stanza (ABA/BCB/CDC)